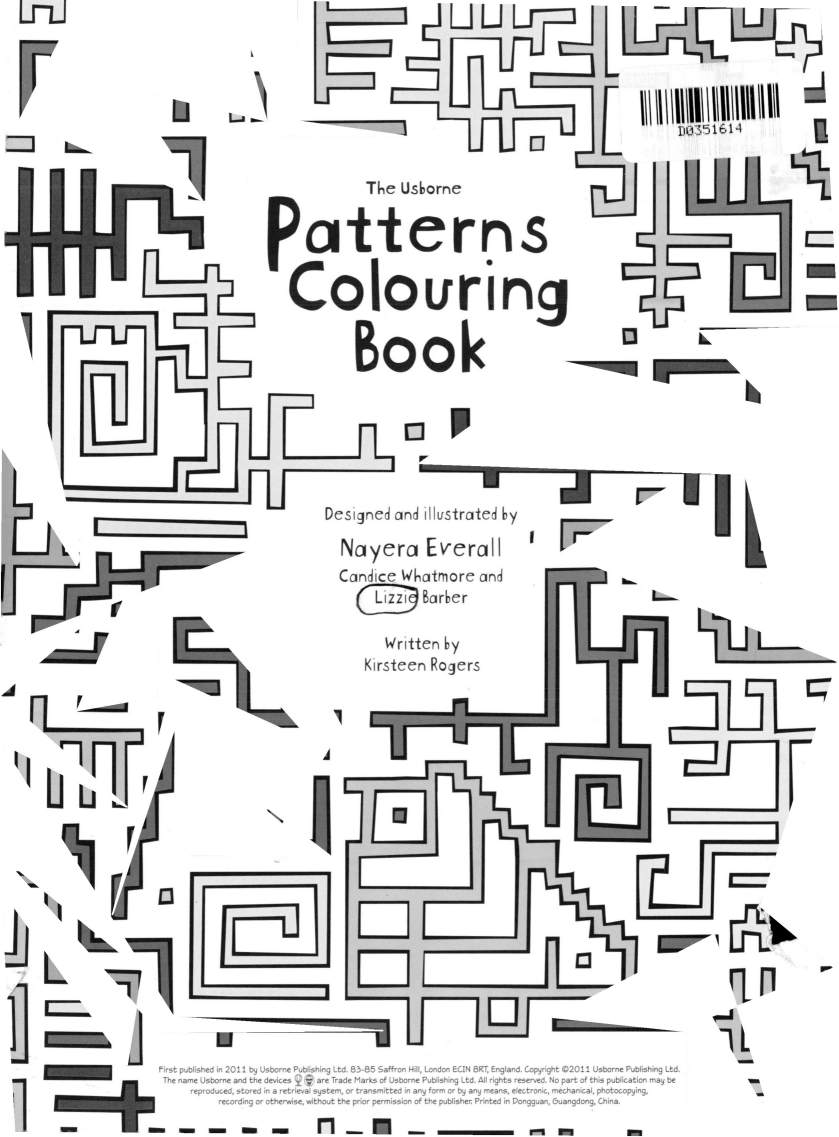

The Usborne
Patterns
Colouring
Book

Designed and illustrated by

Nayera Everall
Candice Whatmore and
Lizzie Barber

Written by
Kirsteen Rogers

First published in 2011 by Usborne Publishing Ltd. 83-85 Saffron Hill, London ECIN 8RT, England. Copyright ©2011 Usborne Publishing Ltd.
The name Usborne and the devices are Trade Marks of Usborne Publishing Ltd. All rights reserved. No part of this publication may be
reproduced, stored in a retrieval system, or transmitted in any form or by any means, electronic, mechanical, photocopying,
recording or otherwise, without the prior permission of the publisher. Printed in Dongguan, Guangdong, China.

How to use this book

On some of the pages you'll find suggestions for how to colour the patterns, but it's your book and you can do whatever you like.

If you'd like to cut out your picture, you'll find a dotted line on each page to cut along.

Use pens, crayons or pencils to fill the patterns. You can colour the designs as they are or draw more patterns in some of the shapes. You could try...

...zigzags and stripes...

...spots and dots...

...stars...

...or anything else you fancy.

You can finish this page to practise colouring.

To fill in large areas like this, use lots of lines going in the same direction.

The colour suggestion panels have dotted lines so you can cut them off if you want to. The white circles are there in case you'd like to try out colour ideas of your own before you begin.

It's a good idea to lay your book on a firm, flat surface while you are colouring.

You could use these colours:

Or try these:

Or use these circles for your own ideas:

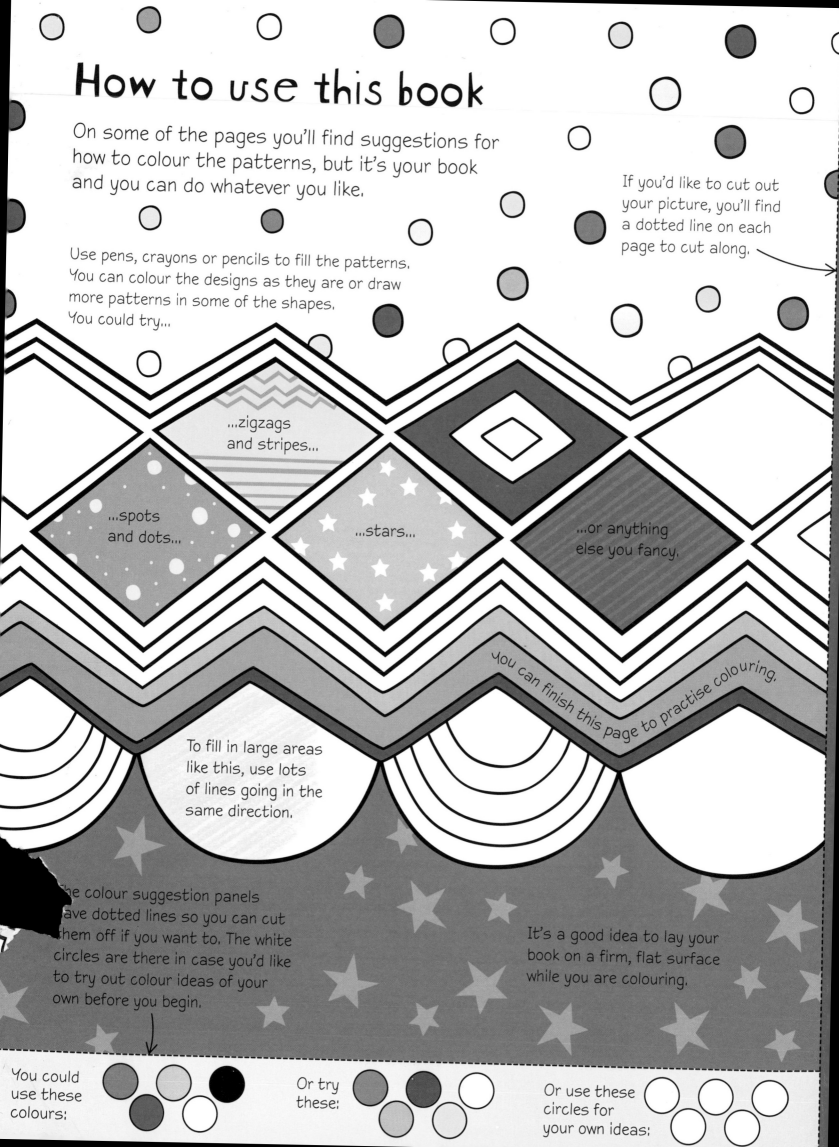

Choosing colours

This bright ring is called a colour wheel and you can use it to help you pick colours. It shows the primary colours red, yellow and blue, and a range of colours in between.

Colours at the edge of the wheel are darker. They get paler towards the middle.

The reds, oranges and yellows on the right of the wheel have a warm, summery character.

Colours on the left of the wheel, such as purples, blues and greens, have a cool, wintery feel to them.

Colours on opposite sides, such as yellow and purple, go well together and make each other seem brighter.

Colour wheel (Red, Blue, Yellow)

Creating different effects

For a gentle, calm effect use colours that are next to each other on the colour wheel.

Choose colours from opposite sides of the wheel if you want an energetic look.

Using only the primary colours red, yellow and blue will give a bold, cheerful pattern.

For a cold effect, use cooler shades, which are on the left of the colour wheel.

To make a pattern feel "warm" choose colours from the right of the colour wheel.

For extra impact, colour some parts of your pattern black, and leave other areas white.

You could see how this pattern looks in warm colours.

Warm colour suggestions:

How about using some cooler colours here?

Cool colour suggestions:

Use whatever colours you like for this pattern.

You can try out your colours here:

These colours will give a cool, calm effect:

These will look bold and dramatic:

Or create a new colour combination:

You can fill these patterns in different ways. Try this one in black and white.

Why not add one or two more colours to this one?

You could see what this pattern looks like in primary colours.

Or choose contrasting colours from opposite sides of the colour wheel.

How about using fresh, springtime colours here?

Or maybe choose some warm autumn shades?

Pick some colours from the same side of the colour wheel.

Use any colours you like to fill this pattern.

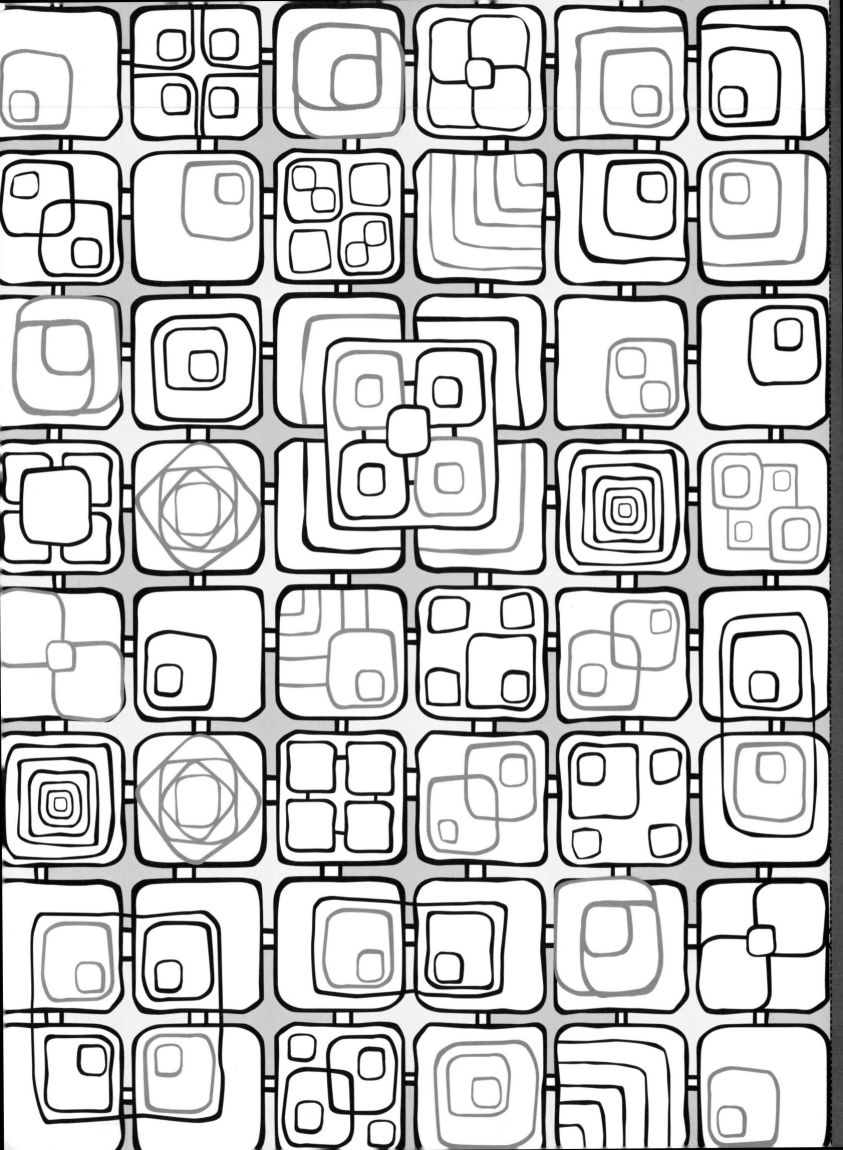

Try filling this pattern with black, white, and two other colours.

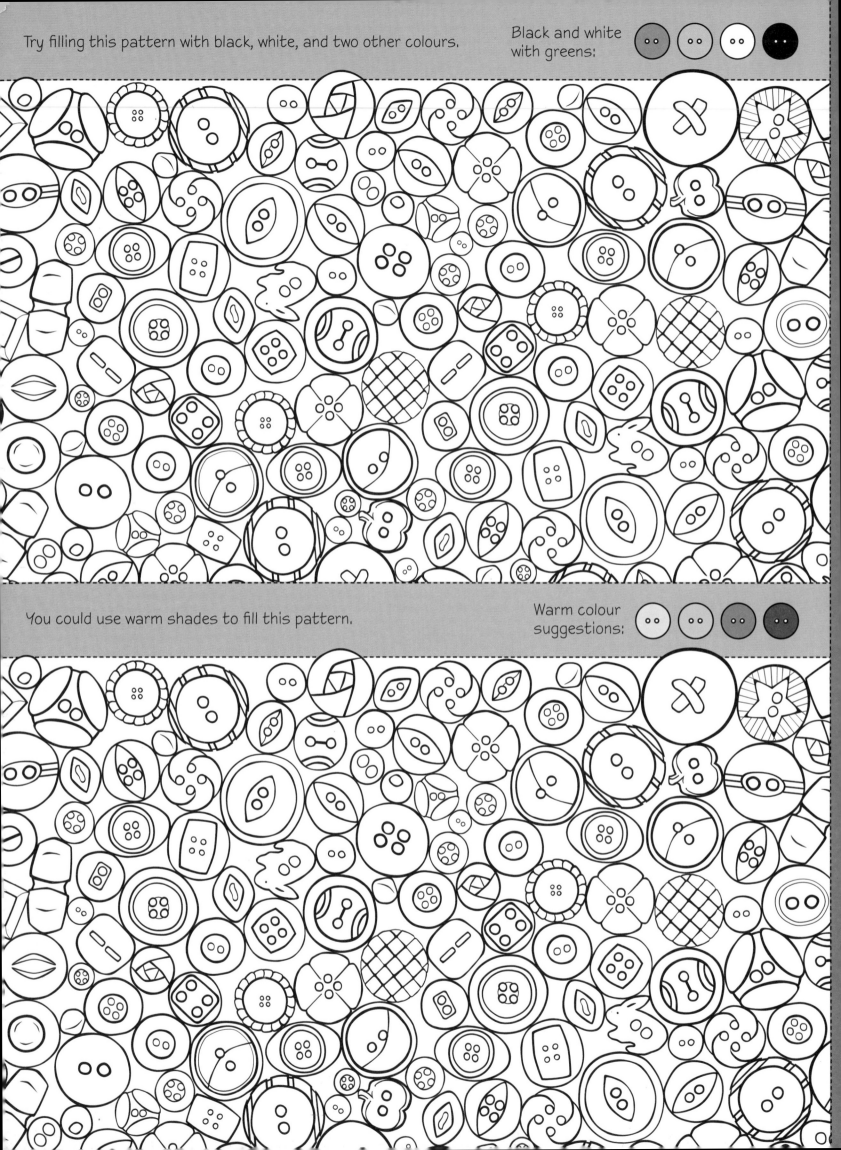

You could use warm shades to fill this pattern.

Warm colour suggestions:

Why not fill this pattern with contrasting colours?

Contrasting colour ideas:

Use whatever shades you fancy for this pattern.

You could test your colour scheme here: